D0365001

WITHDRAWN
MUSSER PUBLIC LIBRARY

# Famous Players

cloth: ISBN: 978-1-56163-555-9
paperback: ISBN: 978-1-56163-559-7
Junior Library Guild Edition: ISBN: 978-1-56163-560-3
©2009 Rick Geary
Printed in China

5     4     3     2     1

Comicslit is an imprint
and trademark of

NANTIER · BEALL · MINOUSTCHINE
Publishing inc.
new york

# FAMOUS PLAYERS

## THE MYSTERIOUS DEATH OF WILLIAM DESMOND TAYLOR

WRITTEN & ILLUSTRATED BY
RICK GEARY

Also available by Geary:
A Treasury of Victorian Murder:
Vol. 1, pb.: $9.95
Jack The Ripper pb.: $9.95
The Borden Tragedy, pb.: $8.95
The Fatal Bullet, pb.: $9.95
The Mystery of Mary Rogers
hc.: $15.95
The Beast of Chicago pb.: $9.95
The Murder of Abraham Lincoln
pb.: $8.95, hc.: $15.95
The Case of Madeleine Smith
pb.: $8.95, hc.: $15.95
The Bloody Benders
pb.: $9.95, hc.: $15.95
The Lindbergh Child pb.: $9.95
hc.: $15.95

P&H: $4 1st item, $1 each addt'l.


We have over 200 titles, write
for our color catalog:
NBM
40 Exchange Pl., Suite 1308,
New York, NY 10005
see our website at
www.nbmpublishing.com

# FAMOUS PLAYERS

## BIBLIOGRAPHY

Anger, Kenneth, *Hollywood Babylon*. (San Francisco, Straight Arrow Books, 1975)

Gardner, Erle Stanley, "William Desmond Taylor," reprinted in *Los Angeles Murders*. (New York, Duell, Sloan and Pearce, 1947)

Higham, Charles, *Murder in Hollywood, Solving a Silent Screen Mystery*. (Madison WI, University of Wisconsin Press, 2004)

Lamparski, Richard, *Lamparski's Hidden Hollywood*. (New York, Fireside Books, 1981)

Kirkpatrick, Sidney D., *A Cast of Killers*. (New York, Penguin Books, 1986)

3 0088 00009 6502

JUN 2 2 2009

MUSSER PUBLIC LIBRARY
MUSCATINE, IA 52761

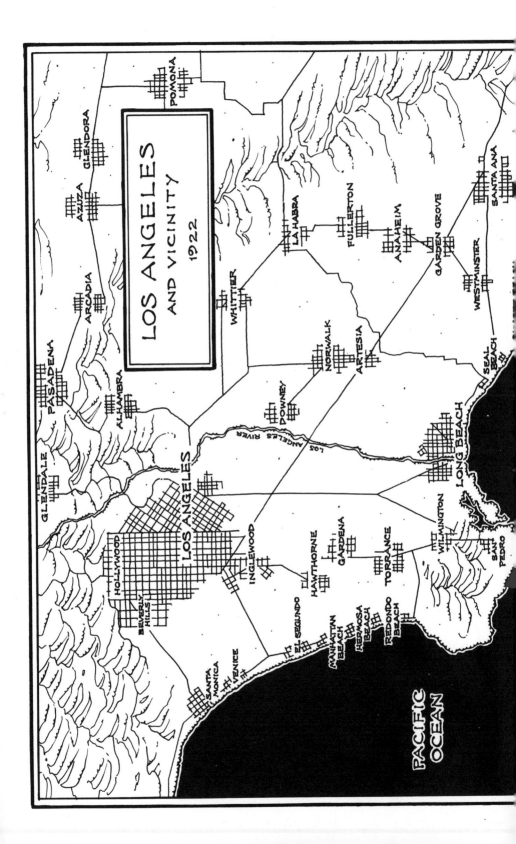

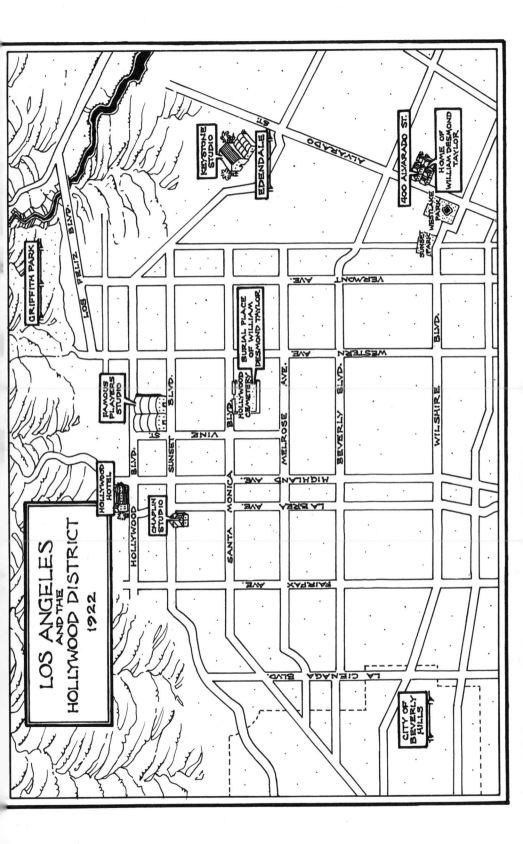

LOS ANGELES
AND THE
HOLLYWOOD DISTRICT
1922

GRIFFITH PARK

LOS FELIZ BLVD.

KEYSTONE STUDIO

EDENDALE

ALVARADO ST.

400 ALVARADO ST.

HOME OF WILLIAM DESMOND TAYLOR

SUNSET PARK / WESTLAKE PARK

VERMONT AVE.

FAMOUS PLAYERS STUDIO

BURIAL PLACE OF WILLIAM DESMOND TAYLOR

HOLLYWOOD CEMETERY

WESTERN AVE.

WESTERN BLVD.

HOLLYWOOD HOTEL

CHAPLIN STUDIO

HOLLYWOOD BLVD.

SUNSET BLVD.

VINE ST.

HOLLYWOOD BLVD.

MELROSE AVE.

BEVERLY BLVD.

WILSHIRE

SANTA MONICA

HIGHLAND AVE.

LA BREA AVE.

FAIRFAX AVE.

LA CIENAGA BLVD.

CITY OF BEVERLY HILLS

# PART I

## THIS IS HOLLYWOOD

WILLIAM S. HART

AS THE 20TH CENTURY DAWNS, THE COMMUNITY OF HOLLYWOOD IS A SLEEPY VILLAGE NESTLED IN THE FOOTHILLS NORTH OF LOS ANGELES ---

A QUIET HAVEN OF ORANGE GROVES AND PUMPKIN PATCHES, HOME TO RETIREES FROM THE EAST AND MIDWEST.

LOTS FOR SALE

BUT THIS IS NOT TO LAST.

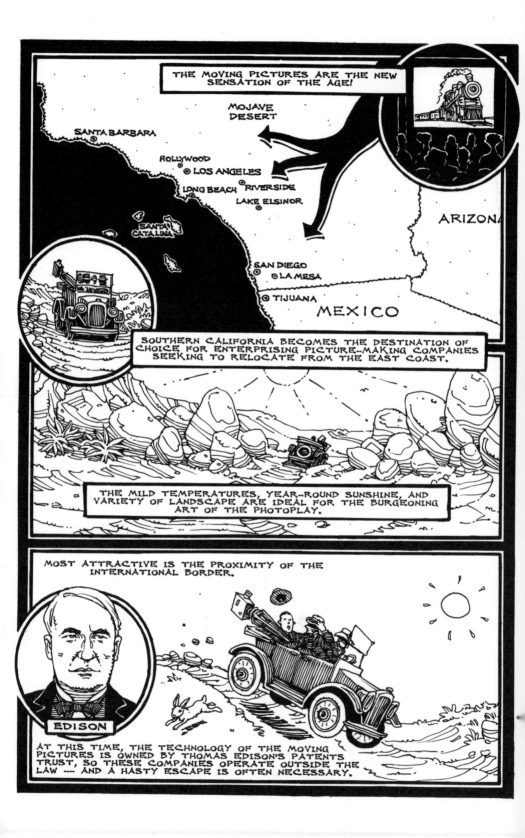

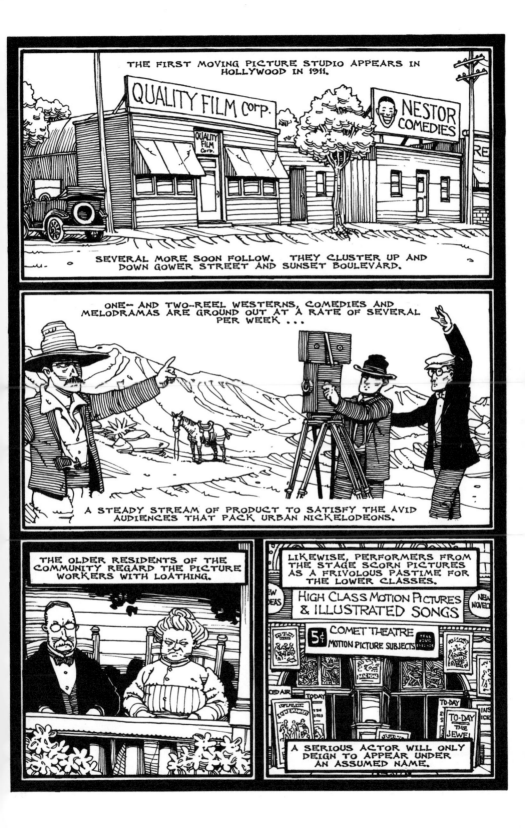

BUT THIS STATE OF AFFAIRS IS NOT TO LAST FOR LONG, AS FEATURE-LENGTH FILMS BECOME POPULAR, AND STUDIOS BEGIN TO EXPAND INTO LARGE-SCALE FACTORIES.

THE DIRECTOR D. W. GRIFFITH RAISES THE PHOTOPLAY INTO RESPECTABILITY WITH HIS GIANT EPICS "THE BIRTH OF A NATION" (1915) AND "INTOLERANCE" (1916).

D. W. GRIFFITH

THE BUSINESSMEN WHO OWN NICKELODEON CHAINS IN THE EAST ARE EAGER TO MANUFACTURE THEIR OWN PRODUCT.

WILLIAM FOX

LOUIS B. MAYER

SAMUEL GOLDFISH (LATER GOLDWYN)

SO THEY MIGRATE WEST AND BUILD THEIR OWN STUDIOS.

CARL LAEMMLE SITUATES HIS UNIVERSAL PICTURES ON A HUGE TRACT OVER THE MOUNTAINS NORTH OF HOLLYWOOD.

THE KEYSTONE STUDIO, FOUNDED IN 1912 BY MACK SENNETT, PRODUCES ANARCHIC COMEDIES FROM ITS HEADQUARTERS IN THE COMMUNITY OF EDENDALE.

ITS MOST FAMOUS PLAYER IS CHARLES CHAPLIN, HIRED BY SENNETT DIRECTLY FROM THE VAUDEVILLE STAGE. CHAPLIN, HOWEVER, DEPARTS TO FORM HIS OWN STUDIO.

SENNETT

CHAPLIN

KEYSTONE COMEDIES

KEYSTONE

● NOW ●
THRILLS
APPLAUSE
LAUGHTER

KEYSTONE'S OTHER POPULAR ATTRACTIONS INCLUDE:

THE RIOTOUS "KEYSTONE COPS"...

ROSCOE "FATTY" ARBUCKLE, AMAZINGLY NIMBLE FOR HIS BULK...

AND THE ECCENTRIC COMEDIENNE MABEL NORMAND.

BY FAR THE MOST PRESTIGIOUS STUDIO IS FAMOUS PLAYERS. THEIR HEADQUARTERS OCCUPIES A LARGE LOT AT SUNSET AND VINE STREETS.

FOUNDED IN 1912 BY ADOLPH ZUKOR, TO ELEVATE THE CULTURAL IDENTITY OF THE PHOTOPLAY: "FAMOUS PLAYERS IN FAMOUS PLAYS."

SARAH BERNHARDT IN "QUEEN ELIZABETH"

ZUKOR

BUT THE BRIGHT PROMISE OF THE FLEDGELING PICTURE INDUSTRY HAS ITS DARK LINING.

FOR MANY OF THESE NEWLY-RICH SHOW BUSINESS FOLK, THE LURES OF ALCOHOL, NARCOTICS AND SEXUAL DALLIANCE PROVE TOO GREAT TO OVERCOME.

THE COMMUNITY'S FIRST GREAT SCANDAL ERUPTS IN SEPTEMBER OF 1921 AROUND THE POPULAR COMEDIAN ROSCOE ARBUCKLE.

HE IS ACCUSED OF CAUSING THE DEATH OF AN ASPIRING ACTRESS, VIRGINIA RAPPE...

HIS FIRST TRIAL, ON CHARGES OF MANSLAUGHTER, ENDS IN A HUNG JURY...

VIRGINIA RAPPE

AT A LABOR DAY PARTY IN HIS SUITE AT SAN FRANCISCO'S ST. FRANCIS HOTEL.

AND AS HE AWAITS THE VERDICT OF HIS SECOND TRIAL, ANOTHER SENSATIONAL CASE MAKES HEADLINES IN LOS ANGELES: THE MURDER OF WILLIAM DESMOND TAYLOR.

# PART II

## THE DISCOVERY OF
## THE BODY

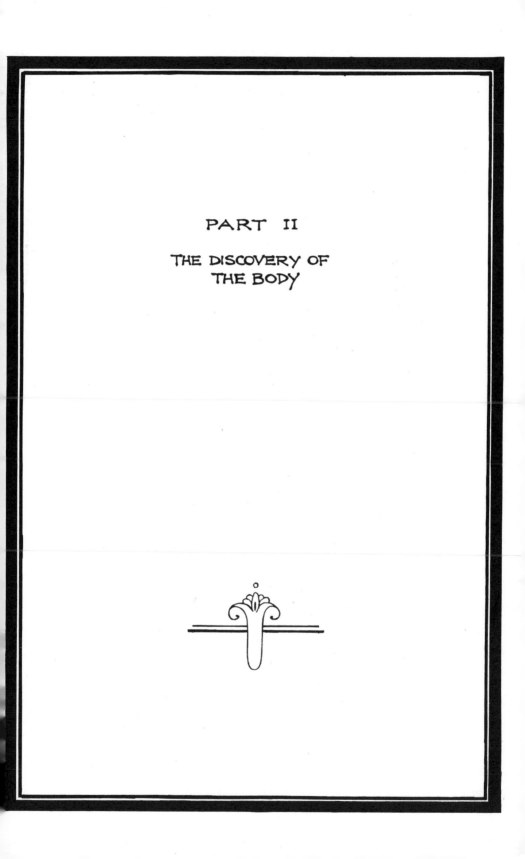

GLORIA SWANSON

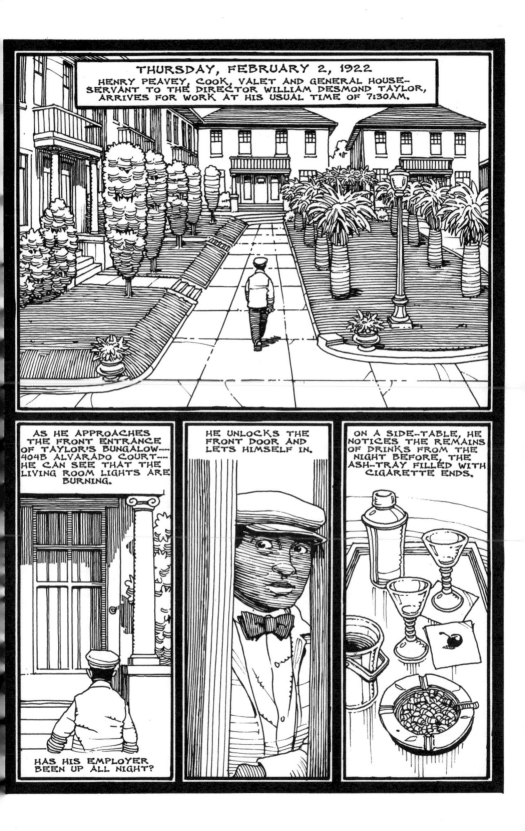

THURSDAY, FEBRUARY 2, 1922
HENRY PEAVEY, COOK, VALET AND GENERAL HOUSE-SERVANT TO THE DIRECTOR WILLIAM DESMOND TAYLOR, ARRIVES FOR WORK AT HIS USUAL TIME OF 7:30AM.

AS HE APPROACHES THE FRONT ENTRANCE OF TAYLOR'S BUNGALOW--- 404B ALVARADO COURT--- HE CAN SEE THAT THE LIVING ROOM LIGHTS ARE BURNING.

HAS HIS EMPLOYER BEEN UP ALL NIGHT?

HE UNLOCKS THE FRONT DOOR AND LETS HIMSELF IN.

ON A SIDE-TABLE, HE NOTICES THE REMAINS OF DRINKS FROM THE NIGHT BEFORE, THE ASH-TRAY FILLED WITH CIGARETTE ENDS.

LOOKING DOWN TO THE RIGHT, HE IS SHOCKED TO THE CORE BY WHAT HE SEES.

THE BODY OF WILLIAM DESMOND TAYLOR, AGE 49, NEATLY STRETCHED OUT ON THE LIVING ROOM CARPET.

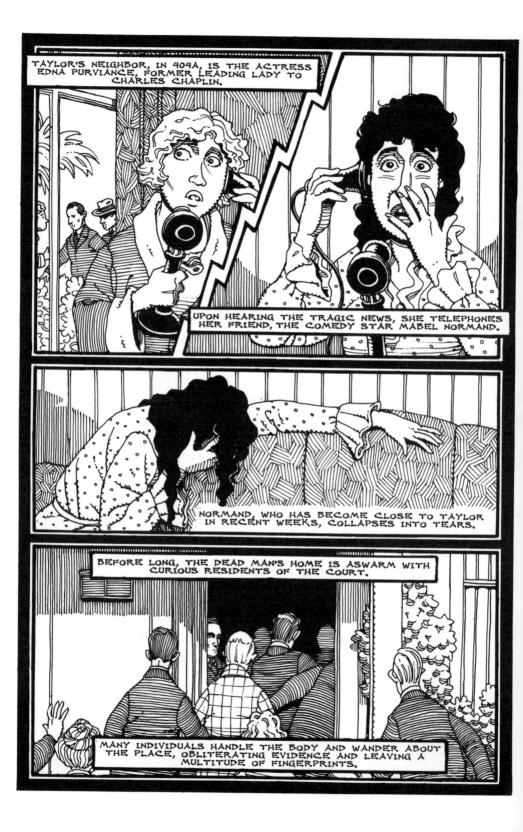

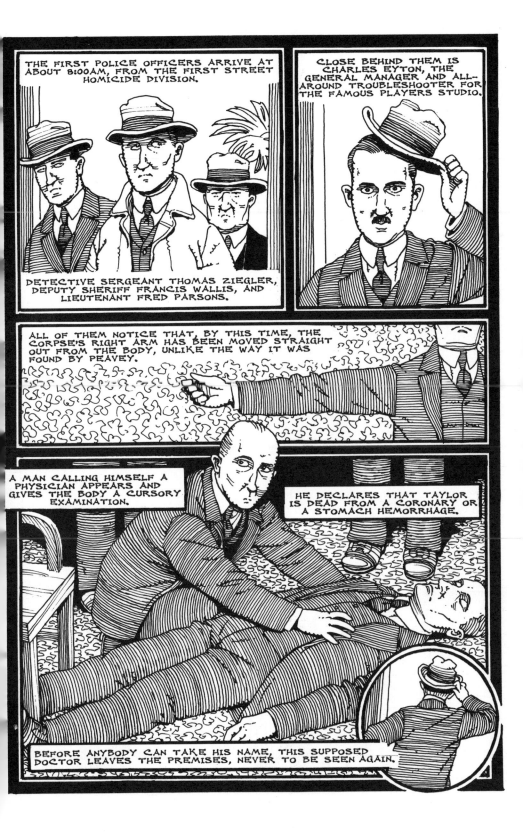

THE FIRST POLICE OFFICERS ARRIVE AT ABOUT 8:00AM, FROM THE FIRST STREET HOMICIDE DIVISION.

DETECTIVE SERGEANT THOMAS ZIEGLER, DEPUTY SHERIFF FRANCIS WALLIS, AND LIEUTENANT FRED PARSONS.

CLOSE BEHIND THEM IS CHARLES EYTON, THE GENERAL MANAGER AND ALL-AROUND TROUBLESHOOTER FOR THE FAMOUS PLAYERS STUDIO.

ALL OF THEM NOTICE THAT, BY THIS TIME, THE CORPSE'S RIGHT ARM HAS BEEN MOVED STRAIGHT OUT FROM THE BODY, UNLIKE THE WAY IT WAS FOUND BY PEAVEY.

A MAN CALLING HIMSELF A PHYSICIAN APPEARS AND GIVES THE BODY A CURSORY EXAMINATION.

HE DECLARES THAT TAYLOR IS DEAD FROM A CORONARY OR A STOMACH HEMORRHAGE.

BEFORE ANYBODY CAN TAKE HIS NAME, THIS SUPPOSED DOCTOR LEAVES THE PREMISES, NEVER TO BE SEEN AGAIN.

MORE POLICE OFFICERS ARRIVE TO GIVE THE HOME A THOROUGH SEARCH ...

ALTHOUGH THEY NEGLECT TO CLEAR THE PREMISES OF THE CURIOUS NEIGHBORS MILLING ABOUT.

CHARLES EYTON IS ALLOWED TO GO UPSTAIRS, PULL OPEN DRAWERS AND CABINETS ...

IN SEARCH OF ANYTHING THAT MIGHT REFLECT POORLY UPON THE DECEASED OR THE STUDIO.

TWO OF TAYLOR'S CREATIVE PARTNERS ARRIVE AT THE SCENE:

THE PRODUCTION DESIGNER GEORGE HOPKINS AND SCREENWRITER JULIA CRAWFORD IVERS.

MRS. IVERS IS SEEN REMOVING A LETTER FROM THE DEAD MAN'S MAILBOX WITH A HAT PIN.

PHOTOGRAPHS OF FAMOUS ACTRESSES ADORN THE APARTMENT, ALL OF THEM INSCRIBED LOVINGLY TO TAYLOR.

MARY PICKFORD

MABEL NORMAND

WINIFRED KINGSTON

MARY MILES MINTER

A MONOGRAMMED HANDKERCHIEF, SUPPOSEDLY FOUND NEAR THE BODY DISAPPEARS, NEVER TO BE SEEN AGAIN.

A SEARCH UPSTAIRS FINDS SEVERAL PASSIONATE LOVE LETTERS TO THE DIRECTOR FROM MISS MINTER.

Dearest
you. I love y

A PINK NIGHTGOWN IS ALSO DISCOVERED IN A DRESSER DRAWER.

IT IS DEEMED A CRUCIAL PIECE OF EVIDENCE AND WRAPPED TO TAKE TO HEADQUARTERS.

A RING CONTAINING NUMEROUS KEYS, THE LOCKS FOR WHICH WILL NEVER BE FOUND.

OUTSIDE THE HOUSE, TOWARD THE REAR, IS SEEN A PILE OF CIGARETTE ENDS IN THE GRASS . . .

AS IF SOMEBODY WAITED THERE FOR AN EXTENDED TIME.

EYTON GIVES TO GEORGE HOPKINS A BASKET OF RECOVERED ITEMS AND ORDERS HIM TO REMOVE IT TO THE STUDIO.

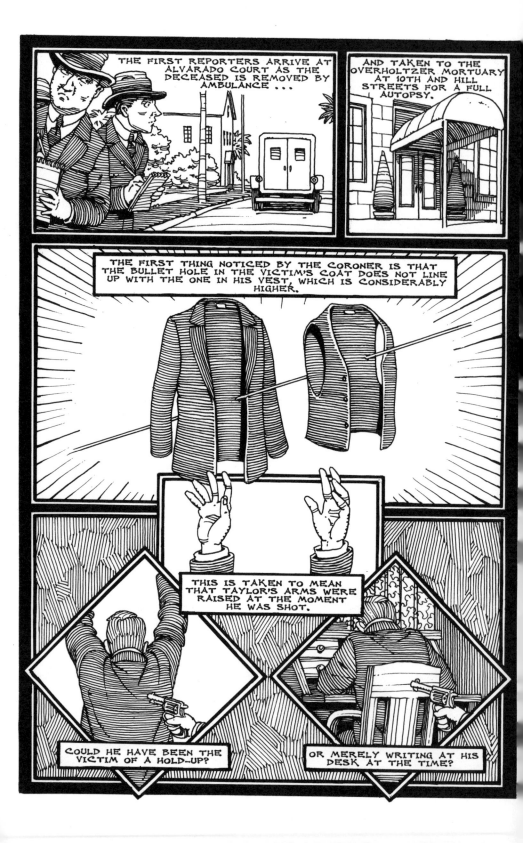

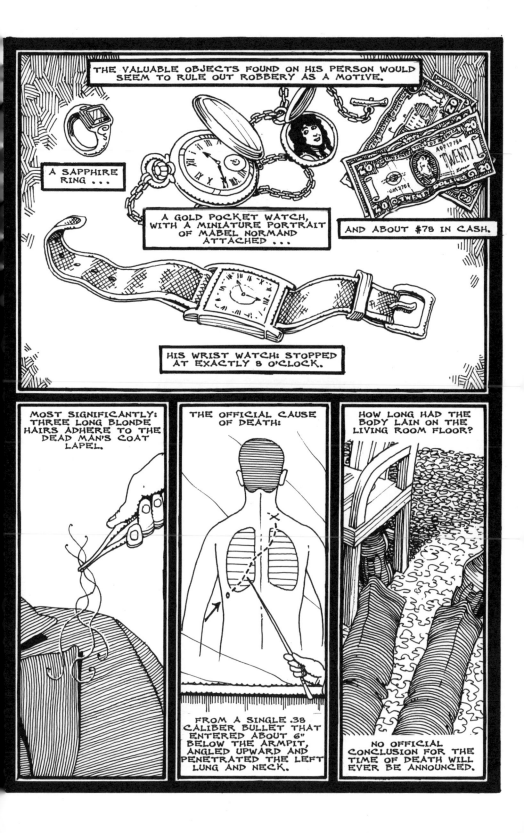

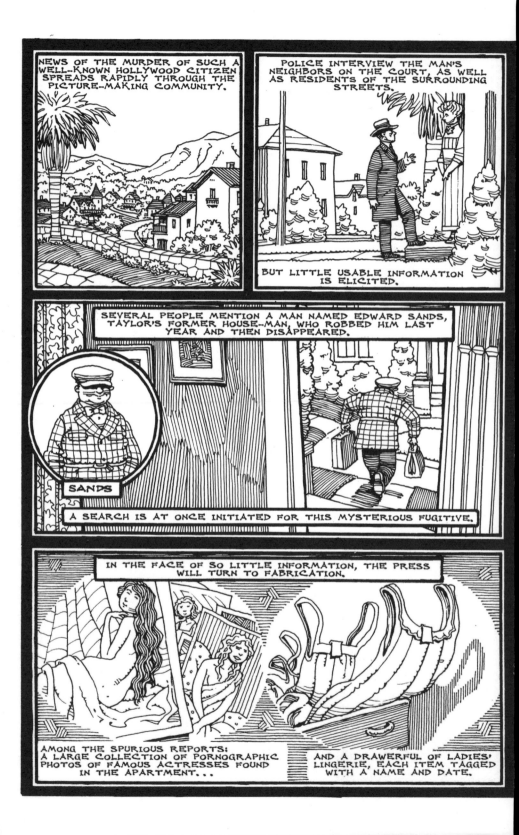

NEWS OF THE MURDER OF SUCH A WELL-KNOWN HOLLYWOOD CITIZEN SPREADS RAPIDLY THROUGH THE PICTURE-MAKING COMMUNITY.

POLICE INTERVIEW THE MAN'S NEIGHBORS ON THE COURT, AS WELL AS RESIDENTS OF THE SURROUNDING STREETS.

BUT LITTLE USABLE INFORMATION IS ELICITED.

SEVERAL PEOPLE MENTION A MAN NAMED EDWARD SANDS, TAYLOR'S FORMER HOUSE-MAN, WHO ROBBED HIM LAST YEAR AND THEN DISAPPEARED.

SANDS

A SEARCH IS AT ONCE INITIATED FOR THIS MYSTERIOUS FUGITIVE.

IN THE FACE OF SO LITTLE INFORMATION, THE PRESS WILL TURN TO FABRICATION.

AMONG THE SPURIOUS REPORTS: A LARGE COLLECTION OF PORNOGRAPHIC PHOTOS OF FAMOUS ACTRESSES FOUND IN THE APARTMENT...

AND A DRAWERFUL OF LADIES' LINGERIE, EACH ITEM TAGGED WITH A NAME AND DATE.

# PART III

# THE FATAL NIGHT

STARS OF THE PHOTOPLAY

DOUGLAS FAIRBANKS

GRADUALLY, INVESTIGATORS PIECE TOGETHER TAYLOR'S ACTIVITIES ON WEDNESDAY, FEBRUARY 1, THE LAST DAY OF HIS LIFE.

NOT FILMING A PICTURE AT THIS TIME, THE DIRECTOR SPENT HIS MORNING AND AFTERNOON ON SEEMINGLY MUNDANE ERRANDS ...

DRIVEN ABOUT IN HIS McFARLAN TOURING CAR BY HIS YOUNG CHAUFFEUR HOWARD FELLOWS.

FIRST, HE DEPOSITED TWO PAYCHECKS AT THE FIRST NATIONAL CITY BANK ...

EAGANS &

AND THEN PAID VISITS TO VARIOUS STORES...

THEN A BRISK SWIM AND LUNCH AT THE LOS ANGELES ATHLETIC CLUB ...

AND A CONSULTATION WITH HIS ACCOUNTANT MARJORIE BERGER OVER HIS TAX RETURN.

(BERGER ALSO HANDLES THE FINANCIAL AFFAIRS OF MABEL NORMAND AND MARY MILES MINTER.)

WHEN PEAVEY RE-ENTERED THE HOUSE, MABEL NORMAND WAS IMPROVISING TUNES WHILE THE DIRECTOR LISTENED APPRECIATIVELY.

AT ABOUT 7:30PM, THE SERVANT BEGAN CLEANING UP THE DINNER DISHES IN PREPARATION FOR HIS DEPARTURE.

(AT THIS TIME, THE CITY OF LOS ANGELES ENFORCES AN 8:00PM CURFEW FOR ALL COLORED PEOPLE.)

HE SECURELY LOCKED THE APARTMENT'S SIDE DOOR AND LEFT THROUGH THE FRONT ENTRANCE.

HE THEN CAUGHT A TROLLEY BACK TO HIS TINY ROOM IN A LODGING HOUSE ON 12TH STREET IN DOWNTOWN LOS ANGELES.

AT ABOUT 7:45, TAYLOR WALKED NORMAND DOWN THE COURT TO HER CAR.

SHE CARRIED WITH HER THE TWO BOOKS THAT HE HAD GIVEN HER...

"ROSA MUNDI AND OTHER STORIES" BY ETHEL M. DELL AND A CRITICAL WORK ON THE WRITINGS OF FRIEDERICH NIETZSCHE.

THE ACTRESS IS DEDICATED TO SELF-IMPROVEMENT, AND THE DIRECTOR HAD TAKEN IT UPON HIMSELF TO SUPERVISE HER EDUCATION.

AS THEY BID FAREWELL AT THE CURB, TAYLOR PROMISED TO CALL HER AT 9:00PM.

(THE FACT THAT HE NEVER CALLED DID NOT STRIKE HER AS UNUSUAL, SINCE SHE KNEW HIM TO BE ABSENT-MINDED.)

THE FEW MINUTES THAT TAYLOR SPENT OUT OF HIS HOME, THE FRONT DOOR UNLATCHED, WILL LATER BE SEEN AS THE PERFECT OPPORTUNITY FOR AN INTRUDER TO ENTER.

THIS STRANGE VISITOR IS AT ONCE ASSUMED TO BE THE KILLER.

SEVERAL WITNESSES COME FORWARD CLAIMING TO HAVE SEEN HIM ON THE NIGHT OF THE MURDER.

AT ABOUT 6:00PM THAT EVENING, A MAN ANSWERING MRS. MacLEAN'S DESCRIPTION APPROACHED HARTLEY'S SERVICE STATION AT 6TH STREET AND ALVARADO ...

GASOLINE

HARTLEY'S

AND ASKED DIRECTIONS TO TAYLOR'S BUNGALOW COURT.

LATER IN THE EVENING, A STREET-CAR CONDUCTOR AND MOTORMAN SAW THE SAME MAN BOARD THEIR CAR ON MARYLAND STREET, NEAR THE CORNER OF ALVARADO.

OTHER CITIZENS RECALL HAVING SEEN A STRANGE OR "NERVOUS-LOOKING" MAN IN THE VICINITY OF ALVARADO COURT.

SOME CLAIM TO HAVE SEEN HENRY PEAVEY SPEAKING TO A MYSTERIOUS FIGURE ON THE SIDEWALK

PEAVEY FERVENTLY DENIES THIS.

# PART IV

## WHO WAS
## WILLIAM DESMOND TAYLOR?

STARS OF THE PHOTOPLAY

THEDA BARA

TUESDAY, FEBRUARY 7, 1922
THE FUNERAL SERVICE FOR WILLIAM DESMOND TAYLOR IS HELD AT ST. PAUL'S EPISCOPAL CATHEDRAL IN DOWNTOWN LOS ANGELES.

A BOISTEROUS CROWD OF TEN THOUSAND FILLS PERSHING SQUARE.

THE DIRECTOR LIES IN AN OPEN COFFIN, ARRAYED IN HIS UNIFORM OF THE ROYAL FUSILIERS.

WREATHES ON DISPLAY INCLUDE THOSE SENT BY RUDOLPH VALENTINO, GLORIA SWANSON, MARY PICKFORD AND DOUGLAS FAIRBANKS

BELOVED MEMORY

OVER THE NEXT SEVERAL DAYS, INVESTIGATORS FOR THE OFFICE OF THE DISTRICT ATTORNEY, THOMAS WOOLWINE, INTERVIEW ALL THE PRINCIPALS OF THE CASE THUS FAR.

WOOLWINE

BY THIS TIME, THE STRANDS OF BLONDE HAIR FOUND ON THE DEAD MAN'S COAT HAVE BEEN POSITIVELY MATCHED TO MARY MILES MINTER.

FOR HOW LONG COULD THEY HAVE ADHERED TO THE FABRIC?

MINTER MAINTAINS THAT, ON THE EVENING OF THE MURDER, SHE WAS AT HOME ON HOBART BOULEVARD WITH HER MOTHER, SISTER AND GRANDMOTHER ...

READING ALOUD FROM THE NOVEL "THE CURSE OF THE KAWA" BY WALTER TAPROCK.

THE ACCOUNTANT MARJORIE BERGER STATES THAT SHE WAS INFORMED OF THE MURDER IN A TELEPHONE CALL FROM MARY'S MOTHER AT 7:30AM THURSDAY MORNING, ABOUT THE TIME THAT THE BODY WAS DISCOVERED.

MRS. SHELBY, HOWEVER, CLAIMS THAT SHE WAS INFORMED OF TAYLOR'S DEATH AT THAT SAME HOUR BY OFFICIALS OF THE FAMOUS PLAYERS STUDIO.

INVESTIGATION INTO TAYLOR'S FINANCIAL DEALINGS UNCOVERS SEVERAL INTERESTING FACTS.

HE IS FOUND, FOR INSTANCE, TO HAVE WITHDRAWN $2500 IN CASH FROM HIS BANK TWO DAYS BEFORE HIS DEATH -- AND RE-DEPOSITED THE SAME AMOUNT ON THE DAY HE WAS KILLED.

MOST SURPRISINGLY, HIS CHECKBOOK REVEALS THAT HE MADE SEVERAL PAYMENTS OF $50 TO A MONROVIA, CALIFORNIA, WOMAN NAMED ADA DEANE-TANNER.

THIS LADY, WHEN INTERVIEWED, CLAIMS TO BE THE ABANDONED WIFE OF TAYLOR'S YOUNGER BROTHER DENIS.

WILLIAM DESMOND TAYLOR, ACCORDING TO HER, WAS NOT WHAT HE SEEMED.

PIECE BY PIECE, DETECTIVES ASSEMBLE AN ENTIRE FORMER LIFE FOR THE MURDERED MAN, WHOSE ACTUAL NAME WAS WILLIAM DEANE-TANNER AND WHO VANISHED FROM NEW YORK CITY IN 1908, LEAVING A WIFE AND YOUNG DAUGHTER.

SHADY PASTS AND ASSUMED NAMES ARE NOT UNUSUAL IN THE WORLD OF SHOW BUSINESS, BUT TAYLOR KEPT HIS A SECRET FROM EVEN HIS CLOSEST FRIENDS.

# THE LIFE OF WILLIAM CUNNINGHAM DEANE-TANNER

HE WAS BORN IN 1872, IN CARLOW, IRELAND...

THE SECOND OF FIVE CHILDREN BORN TO CAPTAIN THOMAS DEANE-TANNER AND HIS WIFE JANE.

HE GREW INTO A HANDSOME AND DASHING YOUTH...

BUT OF A REBELLIOUS NATURE.

HIS FATHER SENT HIM, AT AGE 18, TO "RUNNYMEDE"...

A RANCH ON THE KANSAS PRAIRIE FOR ENGLISH BOYS IN WANT OF DISCIPLINE.

REMAINING IN THE UNITED STATES, WILLIAM BEGAN A NOMADIC LIFE, WANDERING FROM TOWN TO TOWN...

ENDING UP IN CHICAGO, WHERE HE JOINED A THEATRICAL COMPANY.

OVER THE NEXT SEVERAL YEARS, HIS CHISELED VISAGE AND IRISH CHARM ASSURED HIM A BUSY CAREER ON THE AMERICAN STAGE...

PERFORMING UNDER THE NAME CUNNINGHAM DEANE.

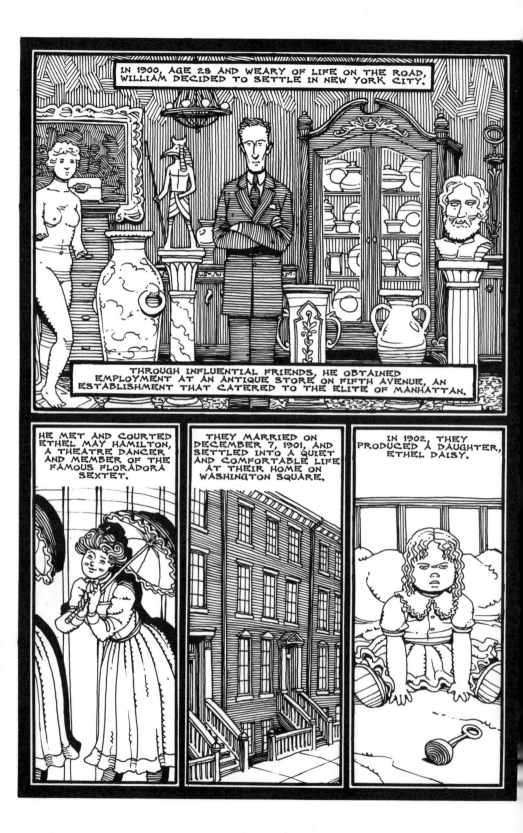

WILLIAM DEANE-TANNER, NOW CALLING HIMSELF WILLIAM DESMOND TAYLOR, BEGAN ANOTHER PERIOD OF WANDERING FROM JOB TO JOB, CITY TO CITY.

HE PERFORMED FOR A TIME WITH A CANADIAN THEATRICAL TROUPE.

HE MINED FOR GOLD IN THE YUKON TERRITORY.

AT LAST, IN 1912, HE MADE HIS WAY TO LOS ANGELES, AND FOUND A PLACE IN THE NASCENT FILM INDUSTRY AS AN ACTOR.

HE ROSE FROM BIT PARTS TO SUBSTANTIAL ROLES, AND IN 1914 GAINED WIDE PUBLIC RECOGNITION AS THE DASHING HERO OF "CAPTAIN ALVAREZ" FOR VITAGRAPH STUDIOS.

HIS WIFE ETHEL, AS SHE WOULD LATER ADMIT, RECOGNIZED HER ERRANT SPOUSE WHEN SHE SAW THE PICTURE IN NEW YORK . . .

BUT SHE DID NOT MENTION IT TO ANYONE, MOST LIKELY BECAUSE SHE WAS THEN ENGAGED TO MARRY ANOTHER MAN.

FROM THE YEAR 1914, TAYLOR GRADUALLY ABANDONED ACTING AND BEGAN A REWARDING CAREER AS A DIRECTOR.

HE ESTABLISHED HIMSELF OVER THE COURSE OF NEARLY FIFTY PICTURES, SPECIALIZING IN ADVENTURE SPECTACLES FOR SEVERAL STUDIOS.

HIS RISE WAS INTERRUPTED BY SERVICE IN THE WORLD WAR. IN THE SUMMER OF 1918, HE ENLISTED, AS A PRIVATE IN THE BRITISH ARMY.

RETURNING THROUGH NEW YORK CITY, HE WAS REUNITED BRIEFLY WITH HIS DAUGHTER DAISY, THEN AGE 16.

UPON HIS ARRIVAL BACK IN LOS ANGELES, IN MAY OF 1919, HE MOVED INTO THE NEWLY-BUILT BUNGALOW COURT ON ALVARADO STREET.

HE TRAINED IN CANADA, ATTAINED THE RANK OF LIEUTENANT, BUT WAS SENT TO ENGLAND ONLY AFTER THE WAR HAD ENDED.

THAT SAME YEAR, TAYLOR BEGAN HIS FRUITFUL ASSOCIATION WITH FAMOUS PLAYERS, WHEN HE DIRECTED MARY MILES MINTER IN "ANNE OF GREEN GABLES."

IN TIME, HE HEADED HIS OWN UNIT, WHICH INCLUDED THE DESIGNER GEORGE HOPKINS (WHO WAS ALSO HIS LOVER), THE WRITER JULIA CRAWFORD IVERS, AND THE CINEMATOGRAPHER FRANK GARBUTT.

HIS INTIMATE RELATIONSHIP WITH HOPKINS WAS KEPT SECRET WHILE HE WAS LINKED ROMANTICALLY WITH A CONTINUING SERIES OF LEADING LADIES.

NEVA GERBER, TO WHOM HE WAS BRIEFLY ENGAGED.

KATHLEEN CLIFFORD

CLAIRE WINDSOR

BETTY COMPSON

MARY MILES MINTER, DIFFICULT AND HIGH-STRUNG, WHO WORSHIPPED HIM WITH AN ALL-CONSUMING DEVOTION.

MOST RECENTLY, MABEL NORMAND, AGE 26, A STAR OF HUMBLE ORIGIN, ATTRACTED BY THE OLDER MAN'S WARMTH AND SOPHISTICATION.

IN SEPTEMBER OF 1919, TAYLOR HIRED, AS COOK AND HOUSE SERVANT, A MAN CALLING HIMSELF EDWARD F. SANDS, AGE ABOUT 23.

THE NEWCOMER OCCUPIED A SPARE ROOM ON THE FIRST FLOOR OF THE BUNGALOW.

IN A SHORT TIME, HE PROVED HIMSELF INDUSTRIOUS AND RELIABLE.

ALTHOUGH AMERICAN, HE AFFECTED A BRITISH ACCENT. BUT HIS CHARM AND HUMOR MASKED A DARK AND ANTI-SOCIAL NATURE.

HE CONCEALED A QUESTIONABLE PAST THAT INCLUDED INSTANCES OF PETTY THIEVERY. IN FACT, AT THE TIME OF HIS HIRING, HE WAS A FUGITIVE FROM THE LAW.

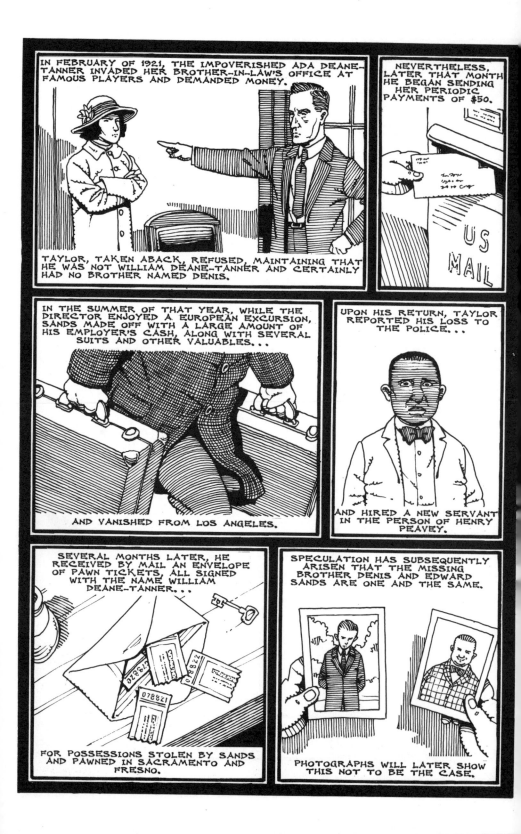

IN FEBRUARY OF 1921, THE IMPOVERISHED ADA DEANE-TANNER INVADED HER BROTHER-IN-LAW'S OFFICE AT FAMOUS PLAYERS AND DEMANDED MONEY.

TAYLOR, TAKEN ABACK, REFUSED, MAINTAINING THAT HE WAS NOT WILLIAM DEANE-TANNER AND CERTAINLY HAD NO BROTHER NAMED DENIS.

NEVERTHELESS, LATER THAT MONTH HE BEGAN SENDING HER PERIODIC PAYMENTS OF $50.

US MAIL

IN THE SUMMER OF THAT YEAR, WHILE THE DIRECTOR ENJOYED A EUROPEAN EXCURSION, SANDS MADE OFF WITH A LARGE AMOUNT OF HIS EMPLOYER'S CASH, ALONG WITH SEVERAL SUITS AND OTHER VALUABLES...

AND VANISHED FROM LOS ANGELES.

UPON HIS RETURN, TAYLOR REPORTED HIS LOSS TO THE POLICE...

AND HIRED A NEW SERVANT IN THE PERSON OF HENRY PEAVEY.

SEVERAL MONTHS LATER, HE RECEIVED BY MAIL AN ENVELOPE OF PAWN TICKETS, ALL SIGNED WITH THE NAME WILLIAM DEANE-TANNER...

FOR POSSESSIONS STOLEN BY SANDS AND PAWNED IN SACRAMENTO AND FRESNO.

SPECULATION HAS SUBSEQUENTLY ARISEN THAT THE MISSING BROTHER DENIS AND EDWARD SANDS ARE ONE AND THE SAME.

PHOTOGRAPHS WILL LATER SHOW THIS NOT TO BE THE CASE.

# PART V

# THE SUSPECTS

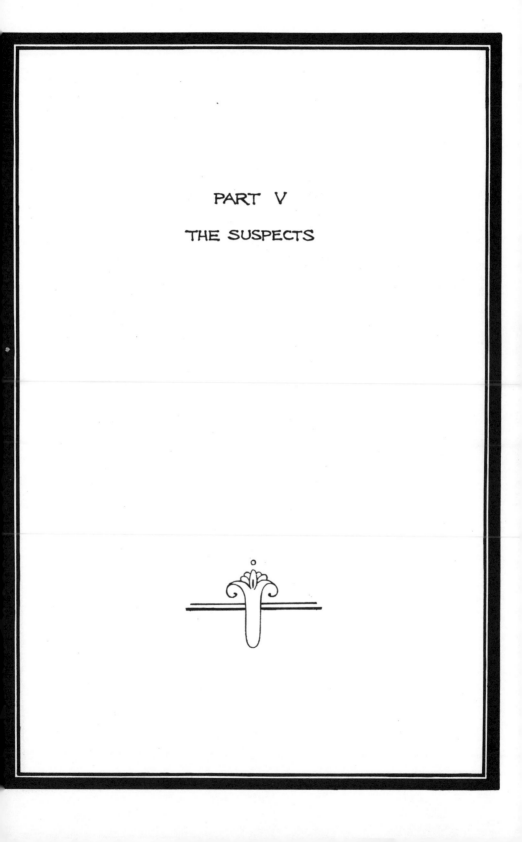

FRANCIS X. BUSHMAN

WILLIAM DESMOND TAYLOR WAS, BY ALL ACCOUNTS, A HIGHLY-REGARDED MEMBER OF THE PICTURE-MAKING COMMUNITY: HONEST AND COURTEOUS, GENEROUS TO ALL...

WITH NO APPARENT ENEMIES, NOR ANYONE WHO WOULD WISH HIM ILL.

BUT THE ONGOING INVESTIGATION NEEDS ONLY TO SCRATCH THE SURFACE.

MARY MILES MINTER, FOR INSTANCE, TURNS OUT TO BE A LESS INHIBITED YOUNG LADY THAN HER SCREEN IMAGE WOULD SUGGEST.

SHE IS KNOWN TO HAVE CARRIED ON DISASTROUS LOVE AFFAIRS WITH: THE DIRECTOR JAMES KIRKWOOD, ACTORS SAM BELASCO, AND MONTE BLUE...

AND THE PENCIL MAGNATE THOMAS DIXON.

IN 1920, SHE MADE A FLAMBOYANT SHOW OF A SUICIDE ATTEMPT...

USING HER MOTHER'S REVOLVER.

HER LETTERS TO TAYLOR REVEAL A PASSIONATE ATTACHMENT. HIS REJECTION OF HER MUST HAVE BEEN PAINFUL.

COULD SHE HAVE COME TO HIS HOUSE LATER IN THE EVENING OF FEBRUARY 1?

THE PATH OF THE BULLET INDICATES THAT THE VICTIM COULD HAVE BEEN IN THE EMBRACE OF A MUCH SHORTER PERSON AT THE TIME.

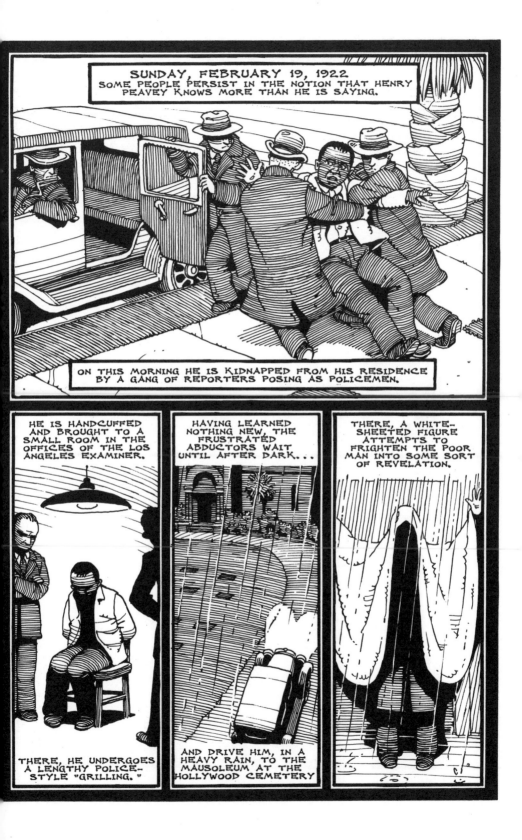

SEVERAL ACCOUNTS EMANATE FROM THOSE INCARCERATED IN CALIFORNIA'S PRISON SYSTEM...

WHO PROFESS TO KNOW THE MURDERER, OR ELSE ADMIT TO THE CRIME THEMSELVES.

BY MARCH, IN FACT, NO FEWER THAN THREE HUNDRED PEOPLE, IN THE UNITED STATES AND ABROAD, HAVE CONFESSED TO THE MURDER OF WILLIAM DESMOND TAYLOR.

THE LOS ANGELES POLICE, DILIGENTLY PURSUING EVERY LEAD, COME TO ONE DEAD END AFTER ANOTHER...

UNTIL AT LAST THE INVESTIGATION SLOWS TO A HALT.

# PART VI

# AN OPEN CASE

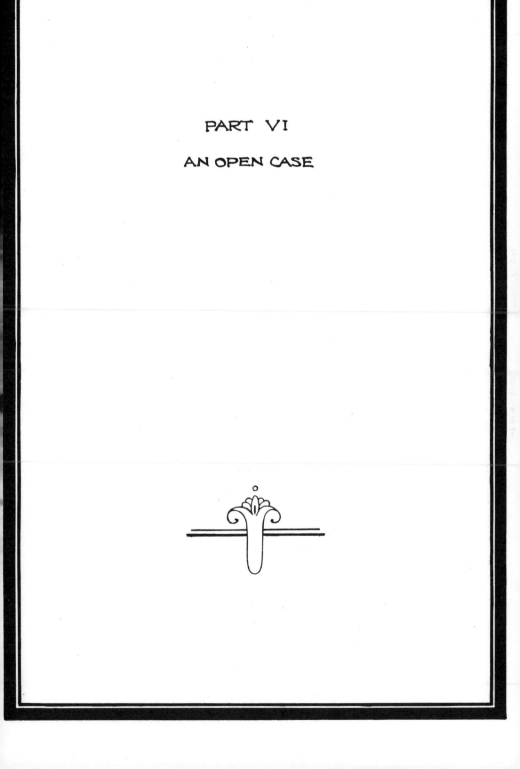

STARS OF THE PHOTOPLAY

LILLIAN GISH

THE YEARS THAT FOLLOW ARE DIFFICULT ONES IN THE HOLLYWOOD COMMUNITY FOR THOSE INVOLVED IN THE TAYLOR MURDER CASE.

BOTH MABEL NORMAND AND MARY MILES MINTER SEE A DECLINE IN THEIR CAREERS, AND NOT ONLY BECAUSE OF THEIR CONNECTION TO THE VICTIM.

THIS WEEK

MINTER MAKES FOUR MORE PICTURES FOR FAMOUS PLAYERS, AFTER WHICH THE STUDIO DECLINES TO RENEW HER CONTRACT.

CLAIMING NEVER TO HAVE BEEN HAPPY AS AN ACTRESS, SHE IS CONTENT TO ALLOW HER CAREER TO END AND HERSELF TO FADE INTO OBSCURITY.

NORMAND CONTINUES STARRING IN FILMS, ALTHOUGH SHE NEVER REGAINS HER PREVIOUS POPULARITY.

HER HEALTH IS DELICATE, OWING TO HER FORMER DEPENDENCE UPON ALCOHOL AND NARCOTICS, AND SHE DIES FROM PNEUMONIA IN 1930, AT AGE 35.

IN 1925, A NEW DISTRICT ATTORNEY, ASA KEYES, DECIDES TO RE-INVESTIGATE THE TAYLOR MURDER.

HE INTERVIEWS ALL THE PRINCIPALS IN THE CASE, INCLUDING MARY MILES MINTER AND HER MOTHER.

BUT IN THE END, HE DECLINES TO ACT UPON ANY OF THE INFORMATION HE HAS GATHERED. AGAIN THE CASE LANGUISHES, UNTIL...

THE YEAR 1937, WHEN MARY MILES MINTER'S SISTER MARGARET SUES THEIR MOTHER FOR MONEY SUPPOSEDLY OWED HER.

506

GRAND JURY

IN THE PROCESS, SHE ACCUSES BOTH MARY AND CHARLOTTE OF INVOLVEMENT IN THE MURDER, BY REVEALING THAT BOTH WERE AWAY FROM THE FAMILY HOME IN THE FATAL EVENING.

ACCORDINGLY, THE CASE IS REOPENED BY YET A THIRD DISTRICT ATTORNEY, BURON FITTS, AND A GRAND JURY IS CONVENED.

BOTH SISTERS AND THEIR MOTHER TESTIFY.

MARY INSISTS, AS SHE ALWAYS HAS, THAT THE LAST TIME SHE SAW TAYLOR ALIVE WAS ON DECEMBER 21, 1921.

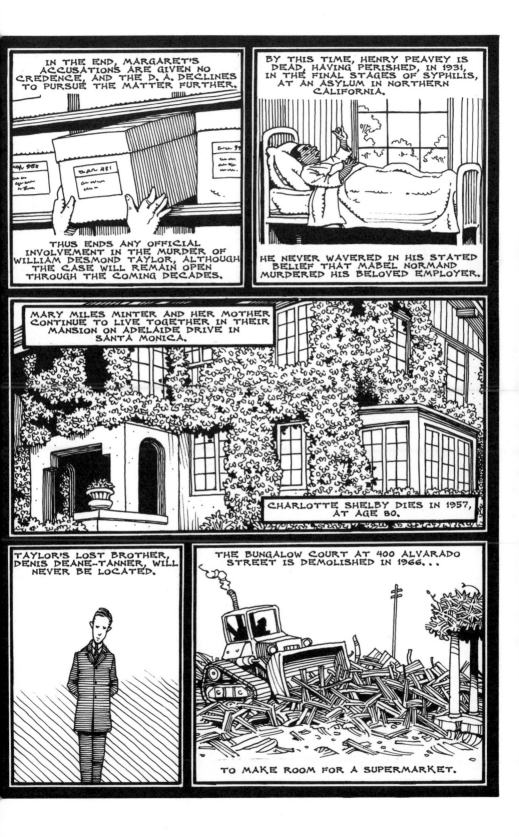

IN THE END, MARGARET'S ACCUSATIONS ARE GIVEN NO CREDENCE, AND THE D. A. DECLINES TO PURSUE THE MATTER FURTHER.

THUS ENDS ANY OFFICIAL INVOLVEMENT IN THE MURDER OF WILLIAM DESMOND TAYLOR, ALTHOUGH THE CASE WILL REMAIN OPEN THROUGH THE COMING DECADES.

BY THIS TIME, HENRY PEAVEY IS DEAD, HAVING PERISHED, IN 1931, IN THE FINAL STAGES OF SYPHILIS, AT AN ASYLUM IN NORTHERN CALIFORNIA.

HE NEVER WAVERED IN HIS STATED BELIEF THAT MABEL NORMAND MURDERED HIS BELOVED EMPLOYER.

MARY MILES MINTER AND HER MOTHER CONTINUE TO LIVE TOGETHER IN THEIR MANSION ON ADELAIDE DRIVE IN SANTA MONICA.

CHARLOTTE SHELBY DIES IN 1957, AT AGE 80.

TAYLOR'S LOST BROTHER, DENIS DEANE-TANNER, WILL NEVER BE LOCATED.

THE BUNGALOW COURT AT 400 ALVARADO STREET IS DEMOLISHED IN 1966...

TO MAKE ROOM FOR A SUPERMARKET.

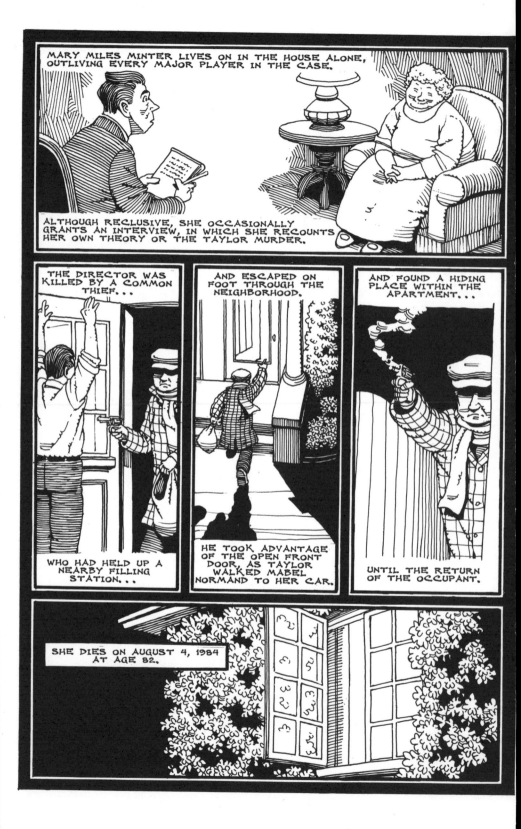

MARY MILES MINTER LIVES ON IN THE HOUSE ALONE, OUTLIVING EVERY MAJOR PLAYER IN THE CASE.

ALTHOUGH RECLUSIVE, SHE OCCASIONALLY GRANTS AN INTERVIEW, IN WHICH SHE RECOUNTS HER OWN THEORY OF THE TAYLOR MURDER.

THE DIRECTOR WAS KILLED BY A COMMON THIEF...

WHO HAD HELD UP A NEARBY FILLING STATION...

AND ESCAPED ON FOOT THROUGH THE NEIGHBORHOOD.

HE TOOK ADVANTAGE OF THE OPEN FRONT DOOR, AS TAYLOR WALKED MABEL NORMAND TO HER CAR.

AND FOUND A HIDING PLACE WITHIN THE APARTMENT...

UNTIL THE RETURN OF THE OCCUPANT.

SHE DIES ON AUGUST 4, 1984 AT AGE 82.

OVER THE DECADES, THE MOTION PICTURE INDUSTRY AND THE COMMUNITY OF HOLLYWOOD UNDERGO MANY TRANSFORMATIONS.

BUT THE TOWN NEVER LOSES ITS PROPENSITY FOR SCANDAL, MYSTERY AND TRAGEDY.

1935
ACTRESS THELMA TODD, AGE 30, ASPHYXIATED IN HER GARAGE.

1944
MEXICAN COMEDIENNE LUPE VELEZ, A SUICIDE AT AGE 35.

1947
THE MURDER OF ELIZABETH SHORT, THE "BLACK DAHLIA."

1955
JAMES DEAN, DEAD IN A CAR CRASH AT AGE 24.

1959
THE SUICIDE OF "SUPERMAN" GEORGE REEVES.

1962
THE DRUG OVERDOSE DEATH OF MARILYN MONROE.

1968
THE DRUG-INDUCED DEATH OF NICK ADAMS, AGE 36.

1976
THE MURDER OF SAL MINEO, AGE 36.

1981
THE ACCIDENTAL DROWNING OF NATALIE WOOD, AGE 42.

1981
THE ALCOHOL-RELATED DEATH OF WILLIAM HOLDEN.

1993
THE DRUG OVERDOSE DEATH OF RIVER PHOENIX, AGE 23.

1998
THE MURDER OF COMEDIAN PHIL HARTMAN.

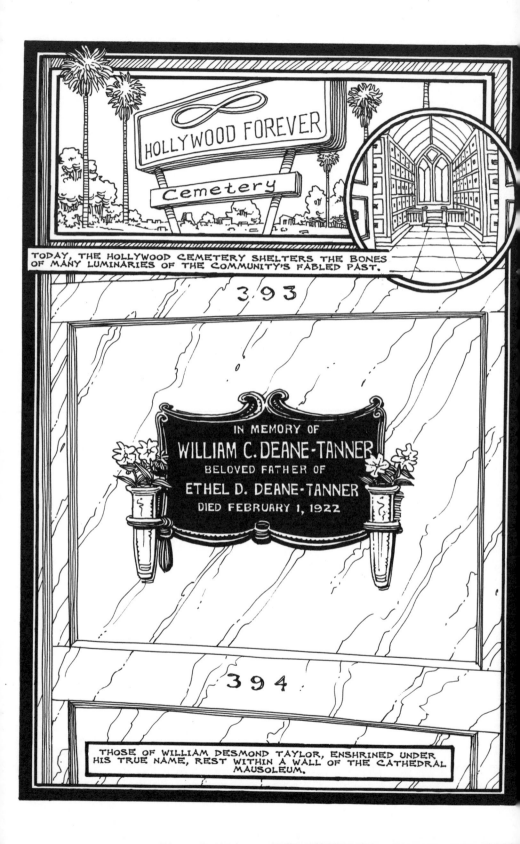

TODAY, THE HOLLYWOOD CEMETERY SHELTERS THE BONES OF MANY LUMINARIES OF THE COMMUNITY'S FABLED PAST.

393

IN MEMORY OF

WILLIAM C. DEANE-TANNER

BELOVED FATHER OF

ETHEL D. DEANE-TANNER

DIED FEBRUARY 1, 1922

394

THOSE OF WILLIAM DESMOND TAYLOR, ENSHRINED UNDER HIS TRUE NAME, REST WITHIN A WALL OF THE CATHEDRAL MAUSOLEUM.